# Read•A•Picture

# LET'S GO

By Burton Marks

Illustrated by Paul Harvey

**Book Express**
Quality and Value in Every Book...

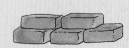

# ON RAINY NIGHTS

On rainy nights when I'm tucked into  ,

dreamy thoughts go through my head.

I hear the patter of the  ,

and look! My 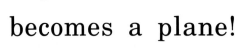 becomes a plane!

It whizzes out the  ,

and soars above the .

I wave to all the passing ,

the , and .

The below looks very small;

I cannot see my at all.

The places where I always play

are tiny from far away.

I journey past the 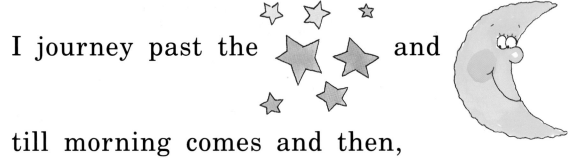 and

till morning comes and then,

my plane flies back into my room,

and becomes my 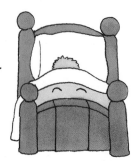 again.

# FIND-A-PICTURE

Somewhere in this picture are:

a [ship], a [train], a [car], a [plane], and a [crane]. Can you find them?

# OFF I GO!

I'm taking a  to Japan,

I'm boarding a ___ for Pakistan,

I'm flying a ___ up to the ___ ,

and I won't be back any time soon.

I'm riding my  to Peru,

I'm driving a ___ to Timbuktu,

I'm sailing a ___ to Bombay,

I must be going—if Mom says it's OK.

# MY LITTLE CAR

I have a shiny little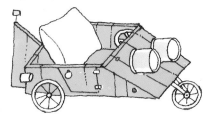

It's ever so much fun.

I never stop to fill it up—

it needs my  to make it run.

# MY "JUST PRETEND" TRAIN

My  is just four kitchen

lined up in a row.

But it can take me anywhere

that I would like to go.

I can cross the highest ,

I can ride down to the sea,

or go deep into the

if that's what pleases me.

I can journey to a

in a land far, far away.

Because my  is "just pretend"

it takes me where I want to play.

# PICTURE A RIDDLE

- What has one horn, runs all day and gives milk?

- What bird can lift heavy things?

- What do you call a sleeping bull?

- What did they call the first bus in America?

- Who has teeth but cannot bite?

- milk truck
- bulldozer
- Columbus
- crane
- comb

# MY BOAT OF WOOD AND NAILS

One day I took some 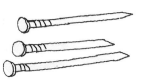 and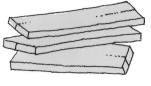

and made a little 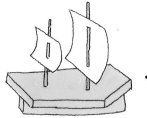 .

I put it in the

to see if it would float.

It drifted quickly out to sea,

the  caught in its 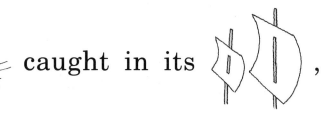 ,

and I never ever saw it again,

my 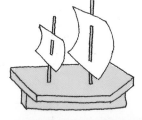 of 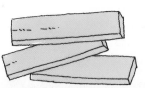 and

# MY VERY OWN SPACESHIP

I'm building my own spaceship

from things I have on hand—

 , rocks, a cardboard 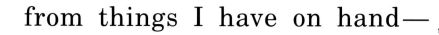 ,

a giant rubber 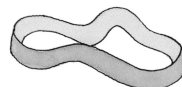 .

Roller 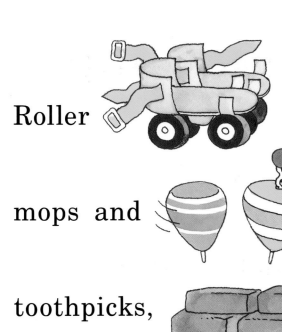 and paper plates,

mops and  and frying ,

toothpicks,  and ice cream sticks,

safety  and garbage cans,

zippers, snaps and bottle 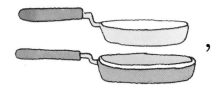,

 and pails and worn-out ,

strings and  and mattress ,

nuts and bolts and metal .

I've been working since this morning
and I cannot figure why,
when I started up the engine
my spaceship wouldn't fly!

I've checked and rechecked everything—
I'm not sure what to do.
Do you think perhaps it needs
another bottle  or **2**?

# LITTLE BEAR'S BIRTHDAY

Little Bear is having a party today.

Look! All the guests are on their way.

Can you name the things
that each one brings?

B+

T+

+D

Presents, presents everywhere.
Happy Birthday, Little Bear!

# FIND-A-PICTURE

Somewhere in this picture are:

a ⬚ , a ⬚ , a ⬚ , a ⬚ , and a ⬚ . Can you find them?

# THE LONG-LEGGED CRANE

Jane McShane is a long-legged

who flies a jet

when she travels to Spain. Unless, of course,

it happens to , in which case

you might see her taking a

# BARNEY MULDOON

Barney Muldoon is a clever

who can play the bassoon by the light of the .

And sometimes in June, in the late afternoon,

he may play you a tune in his hot-air .

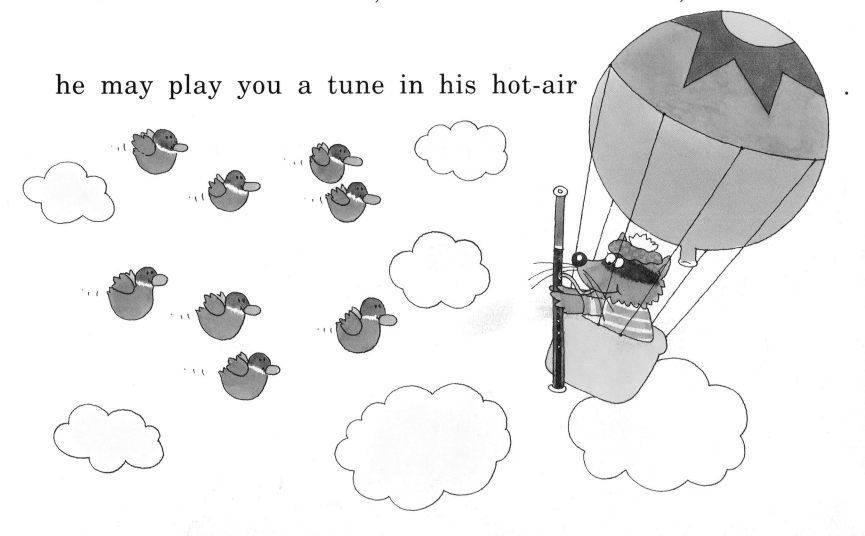

# Read·A·Picture

# ANIMALS

By Burton Marks
Illustrated by Paul Harvey

# THE ANIMALS' PARTY

"But what will we wear?" said Benny the .

"I'll wear my striped ," said Gary the .

"I'll wear my straw ," said Cora the .

"I'll wear my blue ," said Felix the .

"We'll wear our wool ," said 3 smiling .

"I'll wear my silk ," said Millie the .

"I'll wear a , of course," said Harold the .

"We'll wear our red ," said 2 little .

"We'll wear our new ," said the twin .

And that is just what they did.

# LOOK AT ME

Look at me! Look at me!
See all the things that I can be.

I can be an        ,

I can be a        ,

or I can be a

and prowl about the     .

I can be a       ,

I can be a       ,

or I can be a

and fly high in the air.

I can be a

and swing among the

When I play make-believe
I can be anything I please.

# PICTURE A RIDDLE

- What is the safest kind of lion to have around the house?

- What kind of dog do you see at baseball games?

- What kind of key opens bananas?

- What would you get if you cross a pig with a pine tree?

- What animal complains the most?

# TOPSY-TURVY TOWN

Did you ever hear a  meow

or see a polka-dotted  ?

Strange things like that are all around
in crazy Topsy-Turvy Town.

 are smooth as silk

and billy  give chocolate milk.

 laugh, hyenas frown

in silly Topsy-Turvy Town.

 are as small as

and are twice the size of .

don't sting and don't moo

and cock-a-doodle-doo .

 do not make a sound,

and  live underground.

 are green and  are brown

in mixed-up Topsy-Turvy Town.

 can swim and  can fly,

but please don't ever ask me why.
Because *everything* is upside down
in crazy Topsy-Turvy Town.

# WHAT A SHOW!

When the animals put on a show

I hop on my  and off I go.

I laugh when I see the dance,

and clap my as the prance.

The  and

fly through the air;

and a  drives a

with a grizzly

In all the

there are few things I know

that are $\frac{1}{2}$ as much fun

as an animal show!

# PICTURE A RIDDLE

•What animal are you when you take a bath?

•What kind of pet dances and sings?

•What animal are you when you're just too tired to move?

•What does Lassie plant in her garden?

•What kind of crow keeps birds away?

• bear (bare)
• puppet
• dragon (draggin')
• cauliflower (collie flower)
• scarecrow

# MY GARDEN GUEST

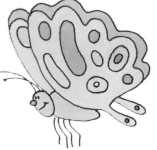

Pretty little

flying through the pale blue sky,

I can't believe that once you were

a fuzzy wuzzy .

# POOR KANGAROO

"What will I do?" said  .

"I cannot find my other 👟 .

My 🧣 and 🎩 are missing, too.

Where can they be? I wish I knew.


There's something funny going on—

my baseball 🏏 is also gone;

my purple  , my teddy 🧸 ,

I cannot find them anywhere.
Where can they be? I've not a clue—
have you?"

Can you help Kangaroo
find his socks and missing shoe?
Can you also help him find his hat,
his bear, his scarf, and his baseball bat?

# ANIMAL TALK

"Good morning," I said to the
animals. "I hope you have a nice day."

The  said, "Gobble, gobble."

The replied, "Neigh, neigh."

The  said, "Bow-wow."

"Moo, moo," said the

The  said, "Cluck, cluck."

"Quack, quack," said the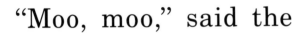

The  said, "Cheep, cheep."

The  said, "Cock-a-doodle-doo."

"Baa, baa," said the  .

And the wise old 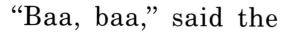 said, "Whoooo?"

And I said, "It's been very nice talking with you."

# PICTURE A RIDDLE

- What animal are you when you're not telling the truth?

- What's the best thing to do if you see a snowball coming towards you?

- What kind of fish twinkles?

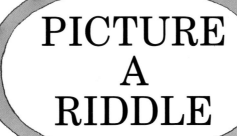

- What is the largest kind of ant?

- What animal are you when you have a frog in your throat?

- lion (lyin')
- giant
- starfish
- duck
- horse (hoarse)

# Read•A•Picture
# RHYMES
# & STORIES

By Burton Marks
Illustrated by Paul Harvey

#  GRISELDA THE WITCH

In a land far, far away, there was once

a witch by the name of Griselda.  lived

in a  near the edge of the forest.

Unlike most witches,  was good and

very kind.

Every morning she made soup out of

and  and gave some to the monsters

who lived in the  .

Sometimes ![witch face] would do magical things.

She delighted in changing ![dandelion] into ![roses] .

But her favorite trick was to change ![acorns]

into ![ice cream cones] , and ![mushrooms] into ![candy canes] .

's days were busy, but sometimes she was

lonely with only the  in the

to keep her company. Then one day a good witch

named Brunilla moved into a  nearby.

 was very excited. That same

afternoon she invited Brunilla to come over

for tea and  and  .

The two witches had a wonderful time.

They rode their 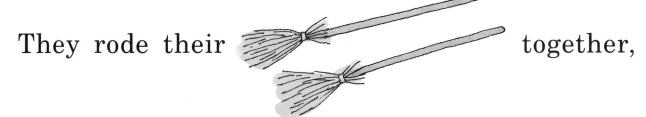 together,

they cast spells together, and they laughed and

told funny stories.

 couldn't have been happier. "How nice

it is to share things with a friend," she said.

# THE BIRTHDAY WISH

If today were my birthday, I'd really like...

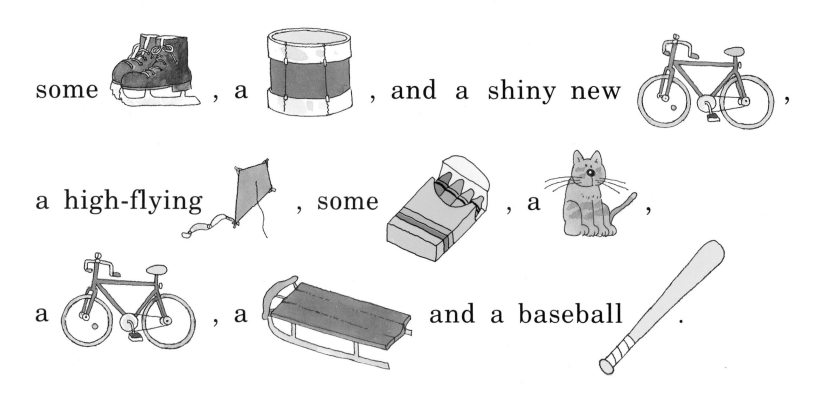

some [ice skates] , a [drum] , and a shiny new [bicycle] ,

a high-flying [kite] , some [present] , a [cat] ,

a [bicycle] , a [sled] and a baseball [bat] .

I know that my birthday is **6** months away,

but I couldn't wait till the very last day

to tell you the things that I'd really like.

By the way, did I happen to mention a

?

# ELWOOD BROWN

Elwood Brown is a sad-faced  .

His face is painted with a frown.

But it's not a  says Elwood Brown,

it's just a  that's upside-down.

# DID YOU EVER

see a
bumble

Did you ever
see a

sipping
tea
beneath
a bola
bola            ?

bake a

while
dressed
up in a
coat and        ?

Did you ever
see a

and an

on a city

in Los Angeles?

Did you
ever
see a

paddle a

with a
wooden
in Kalamazoo?

NOT
ME!

NOT
I!

NOT US!

NO, NO, NO!
DID YOU?

# HUNGRY PETE

A troll I know whose name is Pete
can't seem to get enough to eat.
He gobbles everything in sight
to satisfy his appetite.

He eats the most unusual things

like     and     strings,

and coats and     and    ,

flower     and cuckoo    ,

peels and old tin    ,

plastic     and frying    .

When Pete the troll has guests for dinner
he serves them sand and gravel stew.
And if you are very nice to him
he might have you for dinner, too!

# BEDTIME

Can't I stay up longer?
Just **10** more minutes, please!
We could play a game, and
I'll say my ABC's.

Can I have a  of milk?

Will you listen to my prayers?

Will you read me the  about

Goldilocks and the  ?

Will you bring me a ,

some  and some  ?

Will you see if there's a

hiding underneath my  ?

Can't I stay awake

just **5** minutes more?

Can I have another 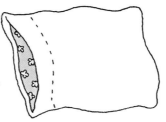 ?

Will you open my  ?

Can I have my

and my 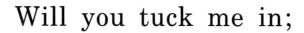 ?

Will you tuck me in;

will you kiss me, too?

If you sing me a song

I won't make a peep.

Please turn off my  .

I...think

...I'm

asleep.

# WHERE IS MY TEDDY?

I'm looking for my Teddy  .

He's hiding in my yard somewhere.

I found my (ball), my (kite), my (boat),
my (car), my (duck), my dolly's (coat).

I even found my rocking (chair).

Why can't I find my Teddy  ?

Can you help find my Teddy Bear?
I know it's hidden here somewhere.
My other things are hidden, too—
I just found them...now can you?

# I'M NOT *THAT* HUNGRY

I'll eat anything you give me.
Every meal will be a treat,
except for one thing I must tell you
that I simply will not eat.

I'll eat  and liver pancakes,

raw  and spinach custard,

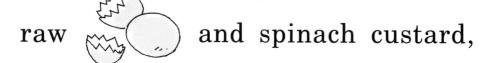 hash and succotash, and

 dipped in mustard.

I'll eat mush and  pudding,

turnip greens and creamed 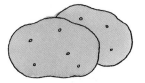 ,

 peels and pickled eels,

artichokes and green  .

Oh, I'll gladly eat all these, and

even olives stuffed with 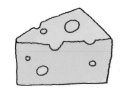 .

 But I beg you on my knees—
please...

don't give me any 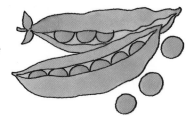 .

# Read•A•Picture
# COLORS &
# NUMBERS

By Burton Marks
Illustrated by Paul Harvey

# COUNTING COLORS

**1** red ,

**2** purple ,

**3** yellow wearing new coats.

**4** blue swimming in the sea,

**5** brown swinging in a .

**6** orange ,

**7** black ,

**8** pink
learning to dance.

**9** green
riding on a train,

**10** white
walking in the rain.

# WHAT THINGS ARE RED?

, and ,

, and .

Ketchup and and candy ,

shiny and raspberry tarts.

Red is a sunset and the in the fall.

Perhaps red is the prettiest color of all.

# FIND-A-PICTURE

Somewhere in this picture are:

**1** **2** **3** **4** and **5** . Can you find them?

# WHAT THINGS ARE YELLOW?

Canaries and and vanilla custard,

and and hot dog mustard!

and and baby chicks,

and and lemon sticks.

Yellow is candlelight, and yellow is the

that shines when I go outside to have fun.

# SUE'S SHOES

One day a  whose name was Sue exclaimed, "I think I've lost a ."

She cried out loud:

Boo hoo, boo hoo! What will I do with just one ?

Just then a called out, "Yoo-hoo," and straight into the room he flew—

Oh, lucky you— I found your .

But my shoe is red.
This 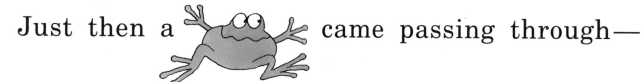 is blue.
It positively
will not do.

That's true, that's true,
but let's review.
Instead of **1**
you now have **2**!

Just then a came passing through—

My dear friend Sue
I brought for you
a purple
now toodle-oo.

Oh dear me!
How can this be?
Instead of **2**
I now have **3**.

And then a  came through the .

I have just what you're looking for— a yellow  almost brand-new.

No more, no more I do implore! Instead of **3** I now have **4**.

But then a  arrived...

Oh dear, I fear here's number **5**.

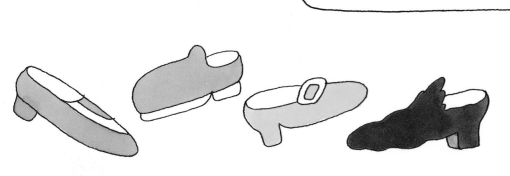

I just heard about your missing  so I brought a new green one for you.

Now Sue was not ungrateful,
and she really was amused
at being the new owner
of so many pretty

Which prompted her to say:

Now I can wear
a different pair
every single day!

# WHAT THINGS ARE BLUE?

Blue jeans, 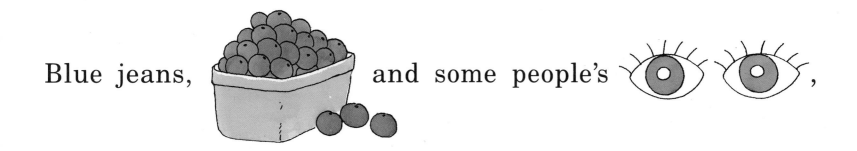 and some people's ,

blue 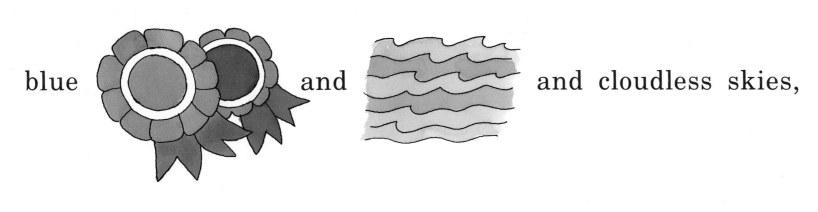 and and cloudless skies,

blue 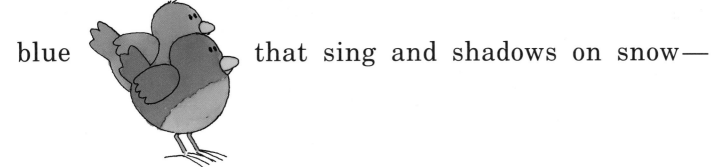 that sing and shadows on snow—

now how many more blue things do you know?

# OWL'S COUNTING GAME

Here's a counting game that's fun. Let's see if you can count to one.

That's easy! I just say **1** shining  and then I'm done.

Now tell me who can count to two.

**1** spool of

**2** loaves of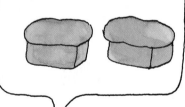

There's just one more thing
I need to know.
Can you count to five?
Ready? Let's go!

**1** red

**2** cuckoo

**3** pairs of and matching

**4** croaking wearing top

**5** barking

chasing **5**

# THE RAINY DAY SURPRISE

Sometimes, on rainy days, Mother gave Tommy

a little surprise. "Will I get a surprise today?" asked

 as the 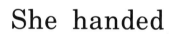 streamed down his bedroom 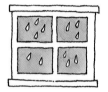 .

"I have a colorful surprise for you," said  .

She handed  a small  . It was a

bright new box of  . "Let's see if you can draw

things that are the same color as each 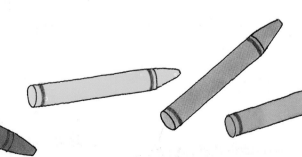 in

the box," said  .

"I'll try," said  . "That sounds like fun."

First Tommy chose a  and drew the  .

Then he took a  and drew a  . Next

he used a  to draw a  and a

to draw  . He used the to draw a .

Finally he used the to draw some .

"Now can you draw a picture using every color

in the box?" asked 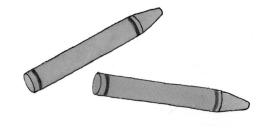 . thought for a

moment, then he started to draw.

Can you guess what Tommy drew?
Turn the page to find the answer.

"That's a perfect picture to draw for a rainy day," said .

# WHAT THINGS ARE GREEN?

 and celery and pickles and 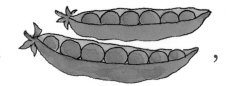 ,

 and  and big leafy  ,

 , olives, cabbage and 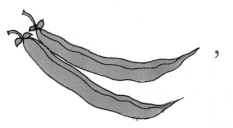 ,

grasshoppers, 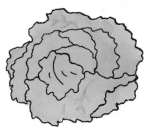 and evergreens.

Green is everywhere, or so it would seem;

how many things can *you* name that are green?

From 1 to 10, from 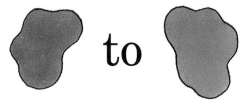 to 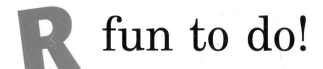,

counting and coloring  **R** fun to do!